C000259638

MALE GROOMING

EVERY BLOKE'S GUIDE TO LOOKING GREAT

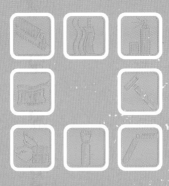

ED WEST

summersdale

MALE GROOMING

Text by Ed West

Illustrations by Salma Conway

Summersdale Publishers Ltd
46 West Street
Chichester
West Sussex
PO19 1RP
UK

www.summersdale.com

Printed and bound by Tien Wah Press, Singapore

ISBN: 1-84024-539-5
ISBN: 978-1-84024-539-4

CONTENTS

INTRODUCTION

THE GROWTH OF MEN'S GROOMING

Once, skin products were considered to be the sole preserve of women, transvestites and sexually suspect glam rock stars, but in the past thirty years all that has changed. In the last decade alone male grooming sales have increased by 800 per cent, so it is now considered fairly normal for men to use perfume, hair care products and even waxing products. A quarter of all British men moisturise, and bear in mind that figure includes the war generation, not many of whom you'd expect to consider collagen levels high on their list of concerns. In the US, chaps spend $4bn (£2.4bn) a year on taking care of themselves, while the British men's grooming market is worth £920m, and is growing at such a rate that by 2008 it is expected to reach £1.5bn. Women fork out half of all money spent on male cosmetics, which at £460m a year must be the most expensive hint in history.

So while male grooming wasn't even shown on film until *Saturday Night Fever* (several years after the first erect penis), today our prime minister admits to spending £300 a year on bathroom products, and even most footballers are metrosexuals, a term coined in 1994 by journalist Mark Simpson to describe straight men who take an interest in their appearance. David Beckham's immaculately cared-for skin and Frank Lampard's waxed chest are a long way from the chain-smoking stars of yesteryear.

WHY BOTHER?

Firstly, and most obviously, because it is beneficial to your health, and likely to keep you looking young and debonair well into old age, while former classmates turn up to school reunions looking like they've spent 12 years in a Bulgarian prison. And since most other men are now looking after their appearance, by failing to keep up with this trend you are giving yourself a distinct disadvantage in the mating game.

But perhaps more importantly, women have more financial muscle these days and are no longer prepared to put up with ill-smelling slobs. Still, there's no need to be a preening ponce; few members of the fairer sex desire a bloke who will hog the bathroom and make *her* wait downstairs fiddling with the car keys while he gets ready. We all need to find the right balance between machismo and sensitivity, and that applies to our looks as much as our personality.

ONE

OUR LARGEST ORGAN

The skin is the largest of the organs, with a total surface area of ten square feet, accounting for 16 per cent of your body weight. And it's not just there to protect us, or because we'd look slightly weird without it – the skin also regulates body temperature, produces vitamin D and hosts the body's glands, so it needs as much care and attention as the liver or the kidneys. The outer layer, the epidermis, is made up of billions of cells that regenerate every three weeks, with 5 per cent dropping off every day, which explains the statistic that 90 per cent of household dust used to be you.

When we become dehydrated, the internal organs steal moisture from their most readily available source: the skin, which contains half of the body's supply of water.

So make sure you spend plenty of time around the office water cooler and drink eight cups a day (three and a half pints, which one in five British people fail to do, according to experts); you'll help your skin and get to talk to women at the same time, finding out all the latest goings-on in *Desperate Housewives* and *EastEnders*, or whatever rubbish was on the previous night.

SOAP-DODGING

Remember to wash your face every morning and evening, but not with soap. Because of its alkaline pH, soap can make the skin dry by removing its natural oils, so buy a pH neutral cleanser. Be sure to avoid soap especially on the face and neck, the most sensitive parts of the body, as it will make them redder over time.

Start the day with a mildly warm shower and quickly alternate between warm and cold; this will increase circulation. Don't spend too long in the water – this will, bizarrely, end up dehydrating your skin.

Turn down the heat in the shower: hot water causes red veins in the skin, and you'll end up with alcoholic features without the pleasures of a lifetime's booze habit. On the same subject, hot water is bad for reproduction. The average 20-year-old British man has half the sperm count of his grandfather anyway, so your wheezing, central heating-bred Generation X sperm could use all the help they can get.

Lying in a bath of Dead Sea salts will not only do wonders for your skin, but make you feel as relaxed and peaceful as if you were actually in the famed salt lake, minus the nearby Israeli/Palestinian conflict. Alternatively, magnesium sulphate, also known as

Epsom Salts, helps to rid the skin of all its poison. Or for some Egyptian-style beauty treatment, add some milk to the bath to remove dead skin – the lactic acid in the milk dissolves the glue holding your dead skin cells to the rest of you.

MOISTURISER

Even a decade ago it would have been unthinkable for a man to rub hydrating cream onto his face or body, yet acceptance of this anti-ageing product now spans all regions and all classes, if not all ages.

There is a wide variety of man-friendly moisturisers available in the shops, so don't just steal your girlfriend's stuff. Men have thicker skin than women (by 22 per cent), and not just in the sense that we are brought up in an atmosphere of bullying and nickname-based torment. Our skin is also oilier (to promote beard growth), more acidic, contains more collagen and has larger pores that create more sweat, so we need different products to prevent its natural tendency to break out in blemishes and spots.

Plus, as men get older, as well as gradually losing interest in the music charts and sex, their bodies produce less of the oils that hinder the ageing process. This is where moisturiser comes in: use it every day after washing on hands and face, to prevent the dry skin that accelerates ageing.

To make matters confusing, there are five different types of skin: normal, oily, dry, sensitive and combination. You'll know you have oily skin if it always has a shiny hue, and this means you should avoid using too much cleanser, cream or anything that makes your skin tingle. Dry skin looks patchy, wrinkles easily, but is rarely afflicted with spots. The dry skin gang should stay clear of soap and alcohol-based toners, and should moisturise more than once a day. Sensitive skin reacts badly to certain chemicals

found in products, and if you have this, give a miss to anything with perfume, including aftershave. Combination skin has aspects of all these types in small doses, while normal skin is not patchy, dry or oily; for these last two types the normal grooming rules should be followed.

You can test your skin's hydration levels by squeezing the back of your hands. If it takes more than a second to return to its normal colour, it needs a drink. But unless you do have dry skin, beware of moisturising more than once a day; overdoing it will strip the skin's layers.

The body and face require different types of moisturiser, which are clearly labelled; that is because the face has the most sensitive skin (and not just so companies can flog us two different bottles) and body moisturiser would be too harsh on it. Also remember, once a week you should give all facial grooming a miss – the rest will let your skin breathe.

THE ELEMENTS

Ever been cycling on a cold day without gloves and come home with bleeding knuckles? This is an extreme symptom of unprotected hands. Ageing skin is often made worse by cold air, which explains the windswept look sported by North Sea fishermen, so wear gloves in winter, otherwise your hands will start to look like they were bought in a market.

The sun is also, sadly, your enemy. As well as giving us skin cancer and turning most Brits into red-faced morons, the sun weathers the skin, which is why young sun-worshipping beach babes eventually turn into walking handbags. In summer, always apply moisturiser or sunscreen with a sun protection factor of 15, whatever your skin colour, and much stronger if you're pale. Dermatologists, that famed scientific community you only hear about in make-up ads, suggest sunscreen should even be used during autumn months, although you shouldn't get neurotic about it. And just to make you feel worse, water, sand and even the pavement all reflect 85 per cent of UV rays, so simply wearing a big hat won't save you (grass, though, doesn't – a handy titbit to mention to any enraged park keepers).

When summer comes, give your legs improved appearance by regularly lying with your feet above your head, improving circulation.

TIP

TWO

SAVING FACE

Treating your face can be a pain in the backside to start with, but no one wants to end up with a complexion like a South American drug trafficker.

EXFOLIATING

This is the very feminine-sounding process of removing dead skin cells with a scrub (a sticky substance that comes in bottles, and feels like liquid sandpaper), and the prevailing view is that you should have a body-wide exfoliating scrub once a week to get rid of dead skin cells, increase circulation and prevent spots. Scrub gently, test first on a less sensitive area, and don't rub your face raw.

If you are really committed about having perfect skin, go to a salon once a month to get a facial, where you'll be pampered with a thorough exfoliation. If you're concerned about the perceived effeminate nature of these places, say something blokey like 'See the football last night?' to the man gently caressing your skin, or have a copy of *Nuts* handy with a comment like 'Phwoar, look at those! I love breasts!' That should remove any confusion.

Once you are done with the face scratching, follow with a moisturiser; on summer mornings use one with sunscreen, while at night apply a moisturiser with AHAs. Alpha-hydroxy acid, or fruit acid, promotes regeneration by removing the top layer of dead, pointless skin (this is the same as dandruff, and anti-dandruff shampoos perform the same service for your hair).

Or, if your face still feels dirty, dab your skin with astringent on some cotton wool to remove dirt and grease, leaving you with skin as smooth as a baby's behind. Women will find it irresistible to touch.

WINDOWS OF THE SOUL

While men are most likely to notice a lady's breasts, backside and face, in that order, for women eyes are the most important feature, and they'll justify the most bizarre romantic choices, from compulsive adulterers to imprisoned serial killers, with the line 'But he has such soft eyes'.

Apply eye drops to increase their whiteness, making yourself look younger and healthier, and at the same time disguising the fact that four hours before arriving at work you were vomiting on the night bus. And always wear sunglasses in the sun; unlike most parts of the body, your eyes can never recover from damage.

EYEBROWS, NOSEBROWS AND EARBROWS

You might act like a caveman with the ladies, but there's no need to also look like one. Pluck any eyebrow hairs that feel the urge to join up with their brethren across the bridge. No woman has gone for the monobrow look since 200,000 BC, and having them will make the girls in the office call you 'Missing Link' behind your back. Also, it goes without saying that nose and ear hair should be monitored (although this is uncommon in young men).

Never shave your eyebrows, as it will simply grow back and in the meantime leave you with monobrow stubble, and don't shave anybody else's while they're passed out drunk. Tweeze them instead – it hurts like hell, but you have to take it like a man.

WRINKLES

In the long term, there are several ways to defend your face from lines:

 Avoid squinting if you're short- or long-sighted, and buy some glasses or contacts.

 Sleeping on a silk or satin pillow ensures smooth-looking skin the next morning… but by that time your date may have sneaked out of your 'creepy' flat – it could be just a bit too effeminate.

 Wrinkles are partly psychological; releasing happy hormones into the bloodstream will reduce wrinkling, and the best way to stimulate these endorphins is through exercise.

In particular, walking is the ultimate defence tactic, as it delivers oxygen to the skin and gets blood flowing.

 Smoking is bad for the skin. As well as causing biological changes that accelerate ageing, the physical act of puffing wears away facial muscles.

BAGS

Bags under the eyes are actually caused by leaking blood from the capillaries – a process known as haemoglobin degradation – that causes oxidation, and a good eye cream will help fix up these capillaries. A good night's sleep, a healthy diet and a less stressful job will also help prevent this haggard look. Yet if you're unable to leave your position as undercover MI6 agent in al-Qaeda but still insist on a fresh under-eye area, try an under-eye concealer. The corner of the eye closest to the nose is the darkest part of the whole face, and most likely to show stress, tiredness or a hangover.

If you can't bring yourself to do that, regularly splashing your face with cold water is the next best thing. It stimulates circulation by causing the fresh blood to move to the surface, and is possibly the only method of grooming that is also a standard feature of most torture methods.

Turn the central heating down. Deepest sleep occurs when the room temperature is between 18 and 24 degrees Celsius.

TIP

Wrap a raw potato in cloth and smash it to bits with a hammer, so that its juices flow through, and this will also help to rid you of under-eye circles (for any farmers out there interested in staying beautiful... who knows, there might be). Spuds contain catecholase, an enzyme used in the cosmetics industry and a natural skin lightener. Simply rub the cloth onto the appropriate area, while avoiding the eye itself, and leave for 15 minutes.

For a short-term eye bag solution, see the Hangover Repair Kit chapter.

If none of this does the trick, see a doctor, as eye bags can be linked to kidney or thyroid problems.

LIPS

Another important area of concern, since women are likely to kiss a soft, juicy set of lips even if the face attached is nothing special (though Mick Jagger's talent and wealth have also helped). Remove flaky skin with a gentle rub of the toothbrush, apply a tiny bit of lip balm, and then pat with tissue. Lips also need the most protection from the sun, since they contain the face's thinnest skin. You can buy special lip sunscreen if you want to avoid the horrible sensation of burned lips.

TIP

Kissing is a good workout for the cheeks, with 34 different muscles involved in just one snog, so regular kissing will keep your cheeks buff. How's that for a chat-up line?

CHIN AND CHEEKS

There may one day be a time when men regularly use foundation, but until that moment comes, you can use your girlfriend's supply under your chin, making it appear far slimmer than it actually is. This is a trick often employed for photo shoots and perhaps not recommended for everyday use.

Hot weather opens the pores and can bring out oily skin; simply run an ice cube over your face and then apply an oil-controlling moisturiser and sunscreen.

THREE

ACNE, BACNE AND COLD SORES

One of the great disappointments of reaching adulthood, and there are many, is finding out that spots never really go away, as a quarter of men are afflicted after their teens – though at least we don't have to deal with pre-menstrual acne. Acne is hormonal, and most theories you hear about it are myths, including its link to fatty food, lack of sunlight, stress, dirt or even watching The Adult Channel.

Acne vulgaris, as it is officially titled, is caused by one particular hormone, androgen, which produces an oil called sebum in such quantities that it mixes with dead skin and bacteria to cause the various types of acne. Blackheads are caused by partially blocked pores, and get their colour from the skin's melanin pigmentation, while whiteheads arise from totally blocked pores and are made white by the fatty acid inside. Then there are cysts (inflamed bumps), nodules (hard bumps), papules (small red spots) and pustules (inflamed pus-filled spots, the evil yellowheads).

Because it is hormonal and not linked to cleanliness, the best you can do is try to alleviate the problem via over-the-counter medication such as benzoyl peroxide, salicylic acid, sulphur and resorcinol, although different treatments work for different people and none for some. If your face still resembles no-man's-land circa 1916, visit your GP, who will probably prescribe antibiotics; but if you're really desperate, many contraceptive pills also cure acne. Obviously that's if you don't mind growing breasts.

Otherwise, here are some tips:

 Use a medicated skin wash, but don't despair if it doesn't work for you.

 Avoid touching your face. Lots of people automatically rub their chin or top lip when talking, which spreads infection.

 Beware of exfoliating on spotty skin; it can cause oils to be released, and spread the zits.

You can reduce back spots (bacne) by wearing cotton rather than man-made fibres.

 Kill blackheads by steaming your face. Fill a bowl with boiling water and lemon juice and hold your face over it, underneath a towel. You have to keep this up every day, otherwise the little blighters will reappear.

 Because the skin produces more oils in hotter weather, spots are more common in summer, so be prepared.

 Dabbing toothpaste on a spot before going to bed may help dry out the skin and eliminate the offending item.

 Alternatively, an intensive dose of vitamin B may help your skin, but it can be extremely unhealthy for your internal organs, causing heart palpitations, high blood pressure and anaemia.

 Finally, if things get too bad, and you have a few quid, laser treatment will finish off the blighters forever.

 Only a third of the population suffer from cold sores, so most of you will be fine, no matter how many dodgy nightclubs you frequent. For the others, rather than trying to disguise it with powder or cream, apply lip balm. This will keep it moist, and increase the likelihood of the cursed thing leaving you in peace.

FOUR

THE SWEET SMELL OF ROMANCE... AND FUNGAL INFECTION

The British spend £380m every year on making men smell nice, and aftershaves are used by three-quarters of us. Which is hardly a surprise when one considers that over 10 per cent of all physical attraction comes down to smell, making it important not to stink like a zoo's gorilla enclosure.

Firstly, deodorant. Today its use seems as mandatory as toothpaste, but as late as 1987, a quarter of men did not even use the stuff. Now we have an amazing array of choices. Generally roll-on deodorant is better for your skin than spray-on antiperspirants, and mineral-based products are best. Deodorants allow the skin to sweat but eliminate the fungus that causes the evil smell. As with food, organic is better for you, but worse for your bank balance.

When it gets very hot, trimming your armpit hair will decrease the stench of hell that comes from this part of your body, to the great relief of your fellow commuters.

TIP

Wearing light-coloured cotton clothing will reduce the amount you sweat in summer (as it absorbs less heat), although the perspiration may be more visible.

Don't overdo the aftershave, and remember that the French writing on the side is not just there to justify its price; eau fraîche is the weakest, followed by eau de toilette, eau de parfum, then perfume. Be careful with the strong stuff, lest you set off an asthma attack in the person next to you (it can happen). Spray it in the air then walk into the scented area for a better balance of smell.

Keep your aftershave inside its box, as light causes chemical changes. Even better, keep it in the fridge.

If you're not sure about the quality or quantity of aftershave, sniff some coffee to awaken your nose before smelling.

FIVE

SHAVING – A MAN'S JOB

Shaving is one of the most underrated teenage rites of passage, and though we might not remember the first time, we can always recall that feeling of being a man at last. Of course, when you get older it just becomes a pain in the backside.

Three things really matter in shaving: a sharp blade, plenty of moisture and the direction.

So have a quick, warm shower before shaving, making the hair easier to cut and opening the pores.

Don't use shaving foam, as it dries the skin; instead try gel or cream. Rub thoroughly, especially below the chin.

You can use a reusable or disposable razor, but use a sharp razor, and the sharpest tend to be the brands with adverts that look like *Top Gun* clips. Throw away once you feel the slightest resistance, as a blunt razor actually shaves the top layer of your skin.

Shave slowly, and don't shave against the grain; this will achieve a closer shave, but you'll end up with an old pirate's complexion. Shave diagonally on the cheek and neck, but horizontally on the chin.

If you're shaving before an important date, don't use a new razor, as these are most likely to cause rashes.

Don't shave in poor light. This might seem obvious, but as well as inadvertently giving yourself experimental Bob Geldof-style facial hair, you'll not notice when the skin reacts to harsh shaving with red patches.

And the rule about all grooming is to treat the neck as part of the face. The skin is essentially the same, and nowadays women have become so particular about hair that they even look out for neck stubble; shave this area every few days.

After the whole business is over, splash with cold water to prevent pollutants getting in, and apply moisturiser.

After shaving, leave the razor in a shallow bowl of mineral oil, and then rubbing alcohol. This will prolong its life, and since a decent blade costs £1.50 a throw, there's no point giving up cigarettes only to spend the same amount of money on a hair removal habit.

And if you live with women, don't leave hairs all over the sink!

TIP *You can remove ingrown hairs with aspirin; crush a couple of the wonder pills and add to a small glass of water, then apply the paste to the offending area before removing with tweezers.*

SIX

EATING YOUR GREENS

Only 13 per cent of British people eat five portions of fresh fruit and veg a day, the recommended daily amount. And remember that unless you can afford to buy organic, the greens you eat are often a pale imitation of their ancestors in terms of minerals and all-round goodness. In fact, we're largely unhealthier today than back in the 1950s, when Britain had rationing and far less food variety, let alone the delights of about 400 TV chefs.

As well as reducing your chances of getting cancer, fruit cleans out your system and prevents the build-up of rubbish in the colon. No one wants to end up like Elvis, carrying around insides with the same structural compositions as concrete, so eat fruit and/or vegetables every day.

Vitamins B, C and E will help your skin. B is found in brown rice, mushrooms, dairy products but most of all in bananas; C in most citrus fruits; and E in nuts, green veg, butter and olive oil.

TIP

Cutting down on salt will reduce eye bags.

Pumpkin seeds, with their zinc, and brazil nuts, with their selenium minerals, could possibly alleviate skin problems. Avocados are also a good source of selenium.

Omega-3, found in fish oils, and omega-6, found in nuts and seeds, will help hair regain life and banish dandruff. Salmon, sardines, mackerel and anchovies are all good aids for healthy hair and skin, as the omega-3 oil keeps both moisturised.

Eat plenty of carrots, greens, sweet potatoes and peaches for the anti-ageing antioxidant beta carotene.

And there's no need to stick to rabbit food either. Red meat, chicken, eggs and fish all contain the antioxidant selenium, which combats both skin

ageing and cancer. Red meat also has plenty of zinc, which keeps the skin clear.

Green tea helps to slow the onset of wrinkles by maintaining collagen; it is also an anti-carcinogenic (cancer preventative) and helps you to lose weight by increasing the metabolism.

Grapes are good skin food, especially red. They contain resveratrol, an antioxidant anti-ageing and anti-cancer agent, as does wine, which is why the French have such low levels of heart disease. Grapes are also especially good for reducing the appearance of veins, as are citrus fruits and cherries.

For those who suffer from a permanently blotchy red face (the condition is called rosacea), it's important to avoid spicy food, hot drinks and alcohol. Well, take the first step and recognise the problem, that's enough for now.

Curry intake should also be moderated during the summer, as it can increase the skin's irritability to sunlight.

And finally, don't become obsessed with diet; thanks to the new male body revolution, 20,000 British men suffer from 'manorexia'.

SEVEN

AMERICAN TEETH FOR BRITISH MEN

Historically, British men haven't had the best reputation for dental care, yet having bad teeth will not only cause a life of pain and cripple us with dental bills, but repulse women too. In poll after poll, women cite good pearly whites as a major requirement, up there with confidence, a sense of humour and a large country estate combined with a hereditary heart condition.

Firstly, floss every night, or after every meal if you wish. Far more important than simply brushing, this removes the plaque that causes gum disease (which has the appropriately unpleasant name gingivitis). Let this build up and the annual gurning competition in Cumbria will soon be the highlight of your social calendar. Eating seaweed is a good way to keep off excess plaque, while for gappy teeth, using an interdental brush will help remove bacteria. If you have really bad breath and nothing will get rid of it, gum disease may be the cause. Ask a dentist.

Invest in cleaning sessions at the dentist twice a year, usually costing £30–50. This might seem expensive, but will save you in the long term, since free dental care is pretty much a thing of the past. And don't be scared of the dentist – many men haven't made a visit to the chair in years, yet technology has made the process far less painful than it was even 15 years

ago, and if you ask nicely, he might let you take away a Superman v Nick O'Teen sticker.

If you have a nagging feeling there's still gunk in your mouth after brushing, buy disclosing tablets for a couple of quid. They'll show up all the plaque in your mouth, allowing you to witness first-hand just how rancid your mouth really is. This also makes for an enjoyable party trick.

TIP

Dehydration is the main cause of furry tongue syndrome, that morning breath feeling after a night of smoking 40 cigarettes; if nothing else works, suck on ginger.

Whiten teeth on the cheap by brushing with grated lemon zest. That way you can avoid the huge expense of seeing a specialist.

But if you want to splash out, and with dental work your teeth could end up worth more than your flat, here are some effective dental treatments:

 Bleaching: A dentist paints gel onto the teeth, using chemicals such as hydrogen peroxide (the same stuff found in hair dye) to penetrate into the tooth and turn it white, giving you that 'Hollywood smile'.

 Microabrasion: A polishing process that gets rid of small stains via a compound rubbed onto the teeth; don't be put off that the main ingredient is hydrochloric acid, as it's painless.

Cosmetic contouring: This evens out your teeth by building the enamel with a sort of dental equivalent of Polyfilla. But at an hour per tooth, it's time- and money-consuming.

 Veneers: These are porcelain sheets grafted onto your teeth, for damaged or yellow teeth.

EIGHT

HANGOVER REPAIR KIT

One of the great advantages that women have in wearing make-up is the ability to disguise a night of shame. In future, those statisticians who total up how much drink costs the economy will have to incorporate spending on men's cosmetics into the figure as men become acquainted with the magical booze-removing powers of make-up.

Firstly, scrub your face with a face cloth to shed some of those boozy top skin cells, or alternatively soak a cloth in cool water and lay it on your face for ten minutes.

Using eye drops with naphazoline will make those boozy old red eyes disappear, but first make sure you don't have an allergy; naphazoline is a medication used to deal with colds, hay fever and conjunctivitis, and though some forms can be bought without prescription, it's strong stuff.

TIP

Chew parsley; it will neutralise your breath. If you don't have this lying around the house, and you probably won't, down a pot of plain yogurt.

Leaving two warm tea bags to soak on your eyes will make them look less tired.

Cucumber slices are also used to help lighten the bits around your eyes, but I wouldn't recommend any man go to such an extent (unless he is certain no one will ever find out).

Moisturise more than usual all around the face, but use special under-eye cream as well, as this area most betrays a heavy night. *Loaded* editor Martin Daubney, who has been known to use this tactic after a heavy night, calls it 'basic Darwinian evolution. Straight guys have learned that if they adopt the ways of the gays they get laid more often.' Blame him if you're caught out at work with it.

NINE

HANDS, FEET AND NAILS

Although many women like a hand that has done a day's graft, they certainly don't like the everyday reality of greasy hands and dirty nails, so put away any notion that having your mitts covered in horse manure makes you as rugged as John Wayne. Which is why more and more men are having manicures and pedicures, and being caught coming out of a salon isn't the instant social death it once was.

Your hands' worst enemy is the sun, which reduces the skin's elasticity and creates ageing marks like wrinkles, brown spots and veins. As previously mentioned, use sunscreen in summer and wear gloves in winter to protect them from the elements.

If you have very dry skin and are really concerned about it, wearing cotton gloves in bed will keep the moisture in, though this may make you look a little eccentric, so best to do it when sleeping alone.

TIP *You can prevent hands getting cold and dry by doing a regular hand exercise: splay your fingers out and then clench, holding for a couple of seconds each time. If it helps, imagine you're a Bond villain explaining how you're going to crush your enemies.*

If you ever do the washing up, use rubber gloves to protect against washing-up liquid. If you feel emasculated by all this, see if you can buy some black gloves with a flame down the side.

And remember that using hand cream doesn't mean you're not a regular lager-drinking, football-loving one-of-the-boys. Soak your hands in warm water and then apply cream. Then hide said cream in a drawer. Applying an anti-ageing hand cream every time your hands touch water will protect your spanners from the toxic pollutants they come in contact with, as well as grease, paint and even bee stings.

Get rid of nicotine stains by rubbing half a lemon onto your fingers and nails for ten minutes.

NAILS

Like hair, nails are made of keratin, a brittle material that feeds on vitamin B and zinc for growth (ideally growing one and half inches a year).

Dry skin, a lack of vitamin C or colic acid can result in hangnails, the useless bits of torn skin that hang off the side of the nail and are irresistible to bite. You can actually buy special cream to rub into your cuticles and hangnails, but don't use scissors on them, or rip them off. Hangnails can be combated by eating the recommended five portions of fruit and vegetables a day and by resisting the urge to bite, while brittle nails can be banished by oily fish, spinach and dairy products, and spotty nails by more red meat (which contains zinc).

Squeezing the top of your finger for a few seconds helps to activate blood circulation and reduces the chances of having hangnails.

While many men are going in for salon manicures, you can do one at home for a fraction of the cost. Firstly trim and file the nail, then rub nail renewal oil into the cuticles and soak fingertips in warm water for a minute or two, all the time massaging your hands. Dry and push back the cuticles (skin border at the base of the nail) with a toothpick, and finally massage with hand cream.

Don't push the cuticles without first warming them up, as these act as the immune system's security guards in this part of the body, protecting the feeble skin below from yobbish infections.

FEET

Apparently the average man walks 80,000 miles in a lifetime, which would be a third of the way from the earth to the moon in the unlikely circumstance that someone built a road through space. And the feet also have a quarter of a million sweat glands, so no surprise then that they sometimes stink a bit. Half of all men have a pungent foot odour, women would not be amazed to learn.

Wash feet every day and let them dry completely before putting on socks. It is also vital to dry between the toes, as the damp is a perfect breeding ground for fungus. If your feet stink, stick anti-foot-odour insoles into your shoes and the smell will go for a few days.

Keep your foot circulation going and you'll avoid athlete's foot, that hellish odour that gives your shoes a distinctive third-day-of-Glastonbury smell.

Avoid wearing shoes indoors and do wear socks with natural fibres.

And avoid wearing the same shoes for days on end; your feet will grow into them, and make any changeover painful.

If you're really desperate about a bad smell, then try either:

 a daily moisturiser with lanolin;

 a daily soak in warm water; and/or

 a massage, starting at the arch and toes before finishing on the calves, helping circulation.

Finally, putting your running shoes in the freezer for three days (in a plastic bag) will kill the stench of trainerfoot, the bacterial illness that seems to overcome most sportswear, even in the terminally lethargic.

TEN

HAIR

Hair care is not just about giving you the trendy appearance of a well-groomed but talentless *X Factor* contestant, but keeping your follicles in good shape, so you don't end up forced to wear an ill-fitting wig in later life.

Get a head massage – it will stimulate hair growth and delay your forehead's war of attrition with your hair.

Dandruff is caused largely by stress or yeast infection, and can be removed by anti-dandruff shampoo or omega-3 oil. If it persists, it may not be dandruff at all but psoriasis (an inflammatory skin condition) or eczema.

> *Make sure you've towel-dried your hair sufficiently before using a blow dryer, however rushed you are to get out of the changing rooms. That way baldness lies.* **TIP**

If your hair feels dirty all the time, it's probably because it's too oily, as oil attracts dirt. Wash your hair with shampoo, but check on the label to avoid products with silicone and panthenol (vitamin B5), which increase oiliness. And though too much use can be a bad thing, forget about the myth that shampoo creates more oil; that's a tale peddled by people who live in tree huts by proposed motorway bypasses.

And finally, if you want nice shiny hair, rinse it in beer. Back in the days before shampoo, people regularly washed their hair in ale, just as milk was used as a straightener. Ketchup and mayonnaise also have their uses, one to remove chlorine after swimming and the other to boost moisture through egg protein (this only works if you use mayonnaise made with fresh eggs). In all cases make sure you rinse thoroughly.

HAIR PRODUCTS

This is one area where you don't want to scrimp, since poor-quality gels will damage your fine locks.

High-quality gel will not only give your hair better shape but also moisturise it, while cheaper products leave you covered in flakes.

Mousse is preferable for men with thin hair, as it adds volume and allows you to manipulate uncontrollable floppy hair, but it's generally more expensive.

If you want to go for a messy bedhead, try pomade (wax) instead, but be prepared for the fact that it takes a couple of washes to get out. And it stains your pillow.

A clarifying shampoo, which has a higher acid content and is designed to remove junk, should be used once or twice a month to get rid of all the products you've put in.

ELEVEN

DON'T BE AN APEMAN – BODY HAIR

Over the last few million years men have been getting progressively less hairy, which suggests that there's a distinct preference in women for hairless men. It is true that some women like an Austin Powers chest on a man, but they're a minority and no female who's made the trip down from the trees wants to grab a hairy back. Unfortunately male evolution hasn't caught up with female desires, so it's up to us to correct nature's mishaps.

Not surprising then that, according to research done by a hair removal brand, a third of men would like to remove unsightly hair but are too scared of the pain or of the stigma of visiting a salon. In America a series of man-friendly salons have opened up, which exude an air of masculinity with customers watching baseball while drinking a Bud as their grooming needs are dealt with – this trend is sure to cross the pond.

There are plenty of areas from where men like to remove hair, foremost being the back, shoulders and forehead, but also the chest, legs and 'bikini line'. For short-term use, simple shaving is best, but though body hair stays shaved for four times longer than its facial cousin, it is still purely a summer holiday solution. However, despite the myth, shaving does not make the hair grow back thicker.

Tweezing requires no more than a pair of tweezers, but should only be used for isolated stray hairs, as it is very time-consuming, and slightly eye-watering.

> *For fair men with dark hair, bleaching is also a possibility, and can be done at a salon (while drinking a Bud, no doubt). The hair is still there, but only detectable very close up.* TIP

But far more painful is **waxing**, a horrendously unpleasant method of hair removal that women have had to put up with for generations. Waxed hair takes between three and eight weeks to grow back, making it ideal for 'bikini lines' (I can't bring myself to use the term without including inverted commas), though it takes a week or so for the rash to die down after the event, so do it a week before your flight. An alternative is to use sugar paper, or depilatories – inexpensive chemicals that destroy the follicles (although some of you may be allergic to them). Turmeric paste, an ingredient in curries, can be applied before a bath and will get rid of the toughest hairs without the ensuing agony of waxing, stripping or whatever other torturous methods women are forced to endure.

For long-term removal, and especially for those with dark hair and pale skin, **electrolysis** might be the answer. Unlike waxing, this destroys hairs at the root (a bit like digging a weed up) and is slightly less painful, but for understandable reasons cannot be tried at home. For even more permanent (and expensive) removal, you can try **laser treatment**, each session costing a couple of hundred quid. A sixth of all laser removals are for men. Men with dark skin should first get tested on a small patch, as the process has been known to lighten the tone, and you could end up with a terrible Wacko Jacko look.

And finally, what about the infamous back, sack and crack? If your lady absolutely demands the full monty, then tell her to get lost. Trimming excess hair in most bodily regions is hygienic and recommended, but we have to keep some things sacred, don't we?

TWELVE

STILL, IF YOU THINK WE HAVE IT BAD...

Before you slam this book against the wall and curse the likes of Brad Pitt for giving women raised expectations, spare a thought for the women who through the ages have been torturing themselves in the name of beauty.

In medieval times, women would bleed themselves to look pale, a hugely effective process right up to the point of fainting/blood poisoning/death.

As recently as the Victorian era, women would apply lead-based make-up on their face in an effort to get that pale and interesting look. The fashion fad, which began as early as the fourth century BC in Greece, led inevitably to lead poisoning.

Not content with that, women from the seventeenth century began applying sulphur and lethal mercury to their cheeks.

To make their eyes brighter, ladies a century later would consume a small amount of arsenic, or wash their eyes with oranges and lemons, or poisonous nightshade juice.

Corsets were often painfully tight, causing the organs to be crushed together; Queen Victoria's waist measured only 18 inches – after she had nine children.

Other cultures can hold their own, though. In China, girls had their feet bound so they wouldn't grow up with clumsy size 10s, while hundreds of years ago the Mayans in what is now Mexico would put girls' heads in vices so they would develop supposedly attractive flat heads.

And all we have to do is throw on a bit of cream. But then we are the weaker sex, after all.

APPENDIX:

A–Z OF GROOMING PRODUCTS AND TERMS

Age-defying formulas – moisturisers that reduce the signs of ageing.

Alcohol-free toner – toners that remove impurities from the skin without removing the skin's natural moisturisers. Alcohol-based products should be avoided by those with dry skin.

Antioxidants – found in healthy green veg, these proteins are the body's version of the Flying Squad, ridding it of dangerous free radicals (pollution and dirt, basically). Oxidation is the chemical reaction that damages cells.

Astringents – these clean the skin of excess oil and reduce the chances of acne.

Collagen – the most common protein in humans (and all mammals), it is responsible for the skin's strength and elasticity, and is used in cosmetic surgery to reduce wrinkles and lines.

Crystal deodorants – the crystals kill off bacteria that cause BO in your armpits by reacting with oxygen.

Depilatories – hair removal cream.

Exfoliant – brushes, sponges or scrubs that remove dead skin, revealing the new cells underneath.

Eye contour gels – products used to protect the areas around the eyes from light, weather, heating and pollution. These areas have no natural protection.

Fruit acid serums – exfoliators that use alpha-hydroxy acid (found in citrus fruit) to bring dead skin unstuck. They break down the inter-cellular bonds attaching dead cells to the skin.

Hydrator – a cream used after shaving to rehydrate the skin.

Lanolin – a form of wax used as a skin ointment that comes from sheep.

Mineral oil – also known as baby oil, a product used in many ointments, cold creams and nail restorers; but is also used as a laxative, fuel for oil lamps, and put in some sweets. Its official name is liquid petrolatum.

Naphazoline – a medicine used to relieve soreness in eyes caused by chlorine, colds and pollution.

Rosacea – a face condition that affects people with fair skin, leading to redness, and is technically a form of acne. Can be reduced by antibiotics, diet change (eliminating alcohol, caffeine, spicy foods) or a less stressful lifestyle.

Rubbing alcohol – substance used to cool or soothe skin, and when diluted can clean minor cuts. Though it's made from ethyl, the same stuff found in your pint, it's highly, highly poisonous and even the lowest tramp wouldn't touch the stuff.

Super antioxidant complex – neutralises the free radicals that cause ageing.

Turmeric paste – an ingredient in curries that has also been used as a healing aid in India so long it appears in a Sanskrit text, the oldest written language on earth. It can be bought in health food shops as well as pharmacies.

Under-eye concealer – cosmetics that hide the ageing process in this vulnerable area.